GRAPHIC LIBRARY™

GRAPHIC SCIENCE

THE BASICS OF

CELL LIFE

WITH MAX AXIOM

SUPER SCIENTIST

Amber Keyser

illustrated by Cynthia Martin

and Barbara Schulz

www.raintreepublishers.co.uk
Visit our website to find out
more information about
Raintree books.

To order:
☎ Phone 0845 6044371
▤ Fax +44 (0) 1865 312263
✉ Email myorders@raintreepublishers.co.uk

Customers from outside the UK please telephone +44 1865 312262

Raintree is an imprint of Capstone Global Library Limited, a company
incorporated in England and Wales having its registered office at 7 Pilgrim Street,
London, EC4V 6LB – Registered company number: 6695582

Designers: Alison Thiele and Victoria Allen
Cover artist: Tod Smith
Cover colourist: Krista Ward
Colourist: Matt Webb
Editors: Lori Shores and Diyan Leake
Originated by Capstone Global Library Limited
Printed and bound in China by South China Printing Company Limited

ISBN 978 1 406 22580 8 (hardback)   ISBN 978 1 406 22584 6 (paperback)
14 13 12 11 10   15 14 13 12 11
10 9 8 7 6 5 4 3 2 1   10 9 8 7 6 5 4 3 2 1

British Library Cataloguing in Publication Data
Keyser, Amber. The basics of cell life. -- (Graphic science) . 571.6-dc22
A full catalogue record for this book is available from the British Library.

CONTENTS

Super Scientist Max Axiom visits an ocean marina to investigate cells.

Cool boat, Uncle Max! What's our mission?

We're going to collect plankton samples for Dr Dineson. She's a cell biologist.

What's a cell biologist?

A scientist who studies cells.

Hey, Nick, help me lower the plankton net.

What do plankton have to do with cells?

Every living thing on Earth is made of cells. Most plankton are made of just one cell.

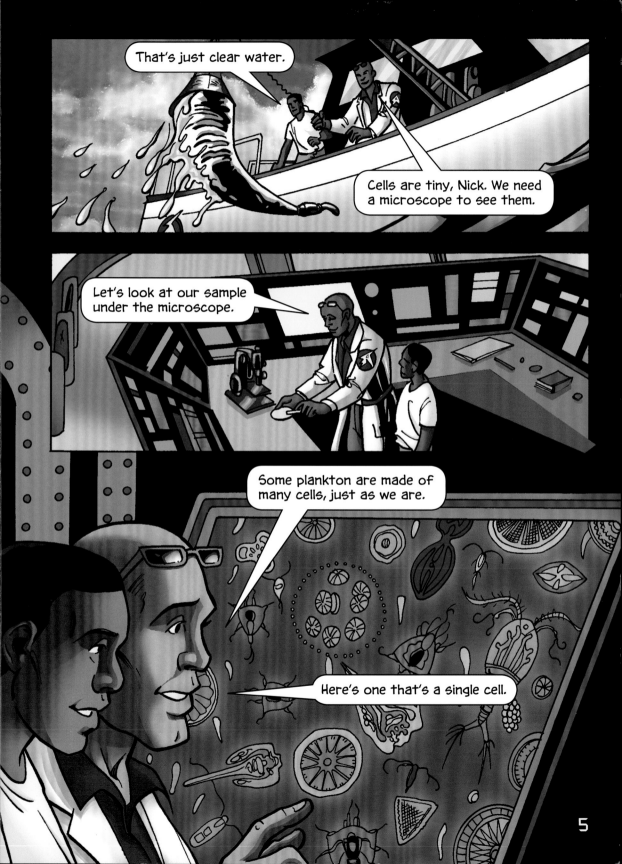

5

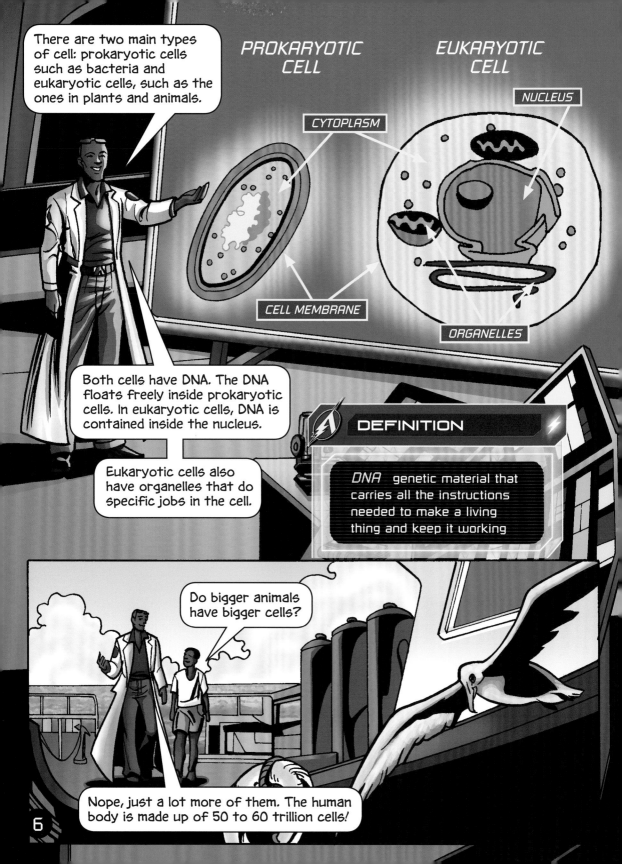

There are two main types of cell: prokaryotic cells such as bacteria and eukaryotic cells, such as the ones in plants and animals.

PROKARYOTIC CELL

EUKARYOTIC CELL

NUCLEUS

CYTOPLASM

CELL MEMBRANE

ORGANELLES

Both cells have DNA. The DNA floats freely inside prokaryotic cells. In eukaryotic cells, DNA is contained inside the nucleus.

Eukaryotic cells also have organelles that do specific jobs in the cell.

DEFINITION

DNA genetic material that carries all the instructions needed to make a living thing and keep it working

Do bigger animals have bigger cells?

Nope, just a lot more of them. The human body is made up of 50 to 60 trillion cells!

Forget cells! Look at that!

I can't forget cells! That sunfish started life as one cell. Then it grew more and more cells to become an ocean giant.

EARTH 3.5 BILLION YEARS AGO

The earliest creatures on Earth were probably prokaryotic cells. Scientists believe all living things evolved from these simple cells.

Understanding how cells work helps us to understand life. Let's get down to their level and check it out!

7

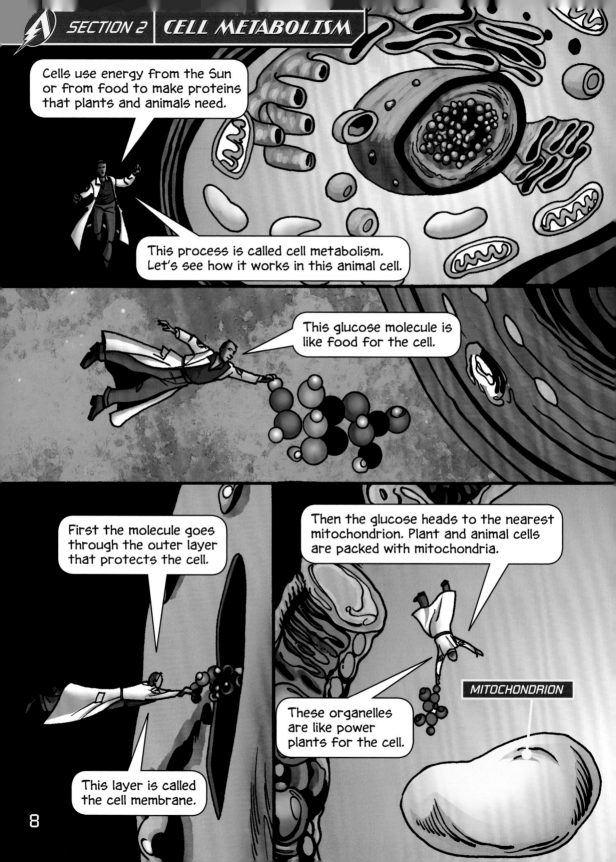

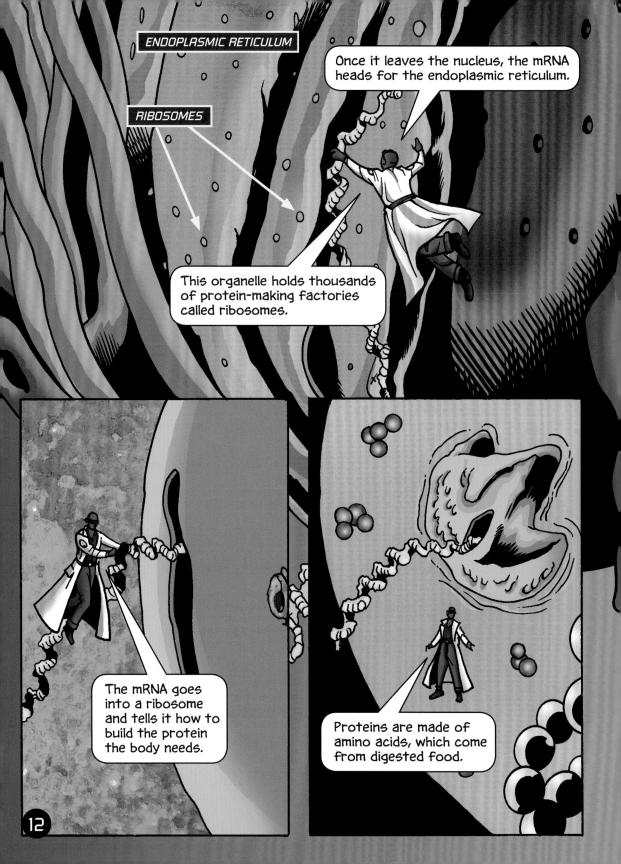

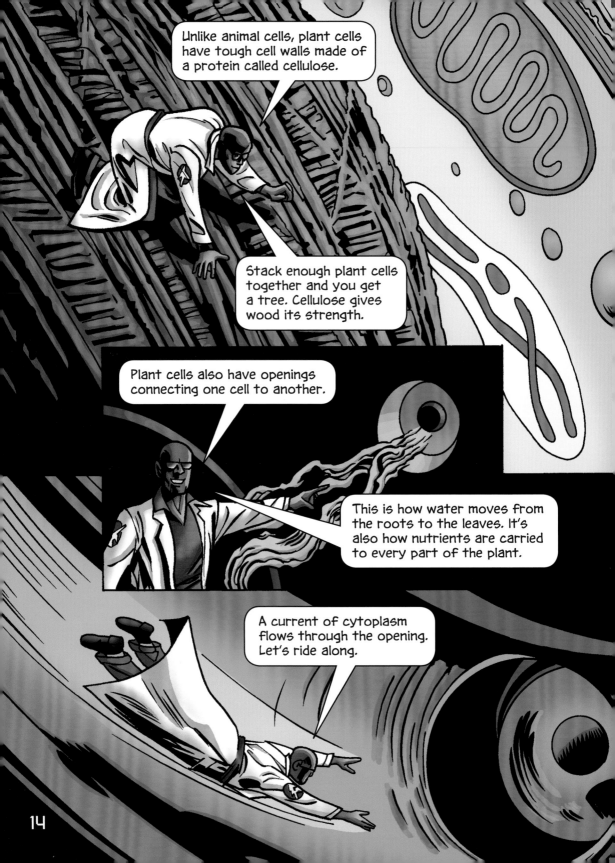

Like animal cells, plant cells have mitochondria to produce energy and ribosomes to make proteins.

And, of course, each cell has a nucleus to run the whole show!

Unlike animal cells, plants make their own food.

This is a chloroplast. You're not going to believe what this organelle can do!

Chloroplasts use carbon dioxide and light to make glucose. This process is called photosynthesis.

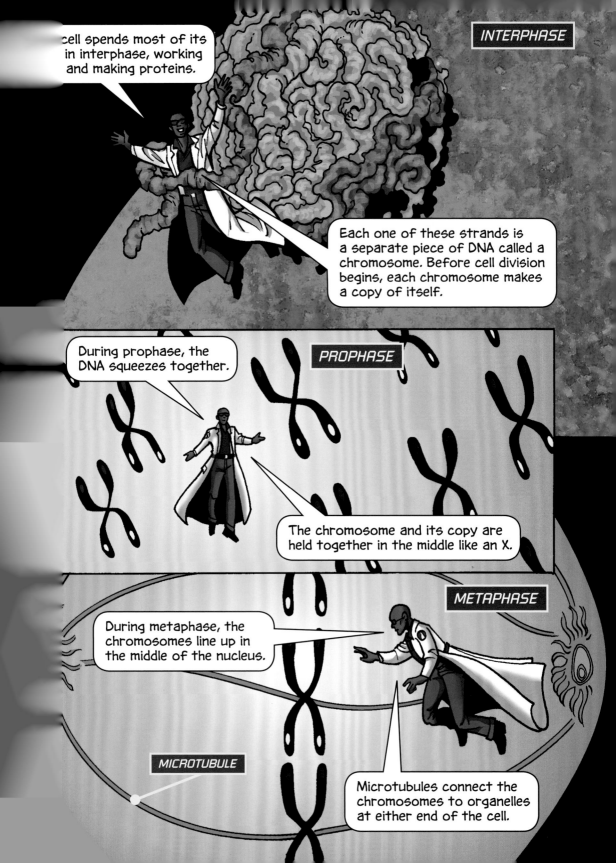

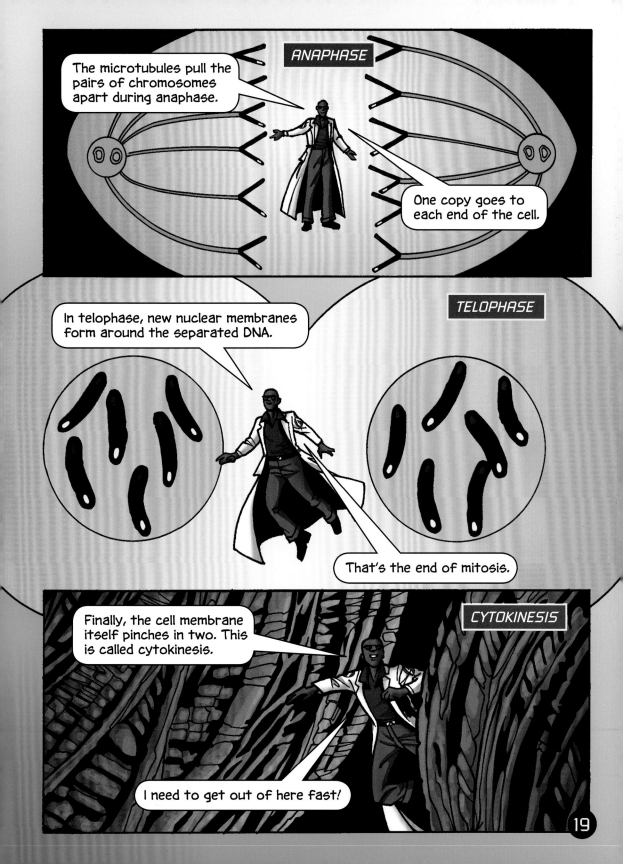

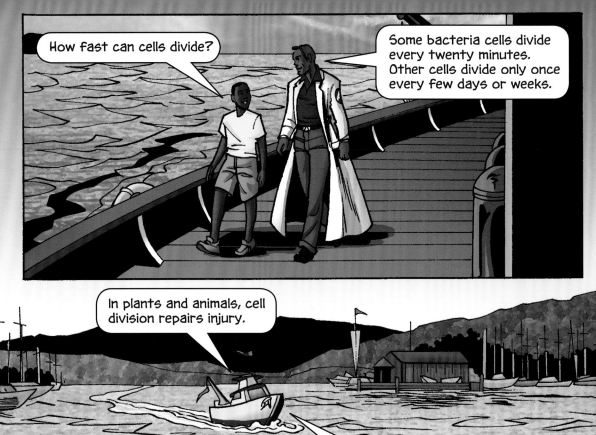

How fast can cells divide?

Some bacteria cells divide every twenty minutes. Other cells divide only once every few days or weeks.

In plants and animals, cell division repairs injury.

Those baby sea lions will grow into adults through cell division, too.

Don't forget, every plant and animal starts as a single cell.

These first cells are called stem cells.

The human body is made of more than 200 types of cells.

In a growing animal, stem cells can become any type of cell during the first few cell divisions.

While Nick delivers those plankton samples to Dr Dineson, let's look more closely at different types of cells!

BRAIN CELL

SKIN CELLS

BLOOD CELLS

FAT CELLS

BONE CELLS

SMOOTH MUSCLE CELLS

STEM CELLS IN MEDICINE

ACCESS GRANTED: MAX AXIOM

Scientists think that stem cells may be the answer to curing many diseases such as Parkinson's and Alzheimer's. Doctors may be able to use stem cells to replace old cells damaged by injury or disease. Bone marrow transplants are a form of stem cell therapy used to treat cancers like leukaemia and lymphoma.

Cells divide constantly on the inside surface of your skin. The new cells travel to the outside surface and produce keratin, a protein that makes the skin waterproof.

On the surface, dead skin cells act like tiny plates of armour protecting us from infection.

The human body has more than 650 different muscles. Each one is made of thousands of muscle cells.

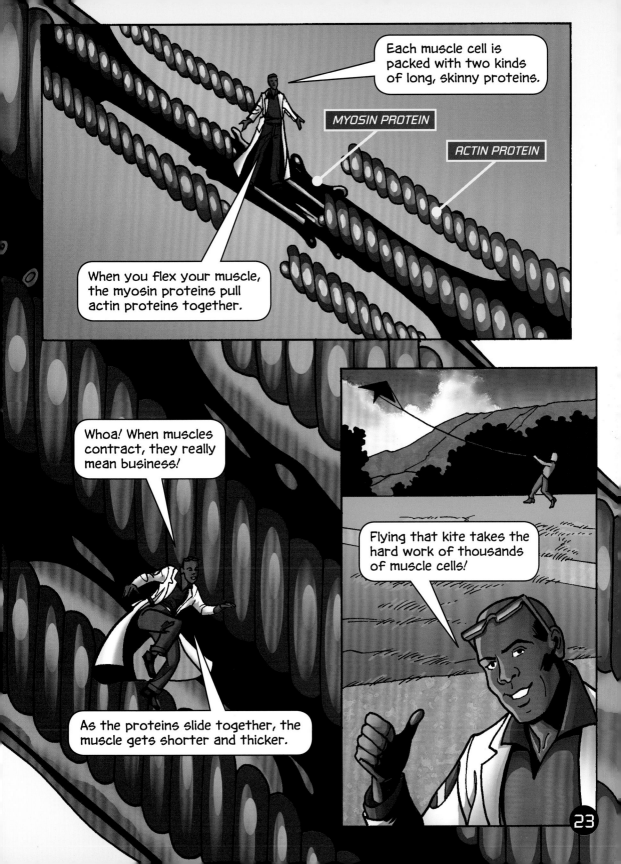

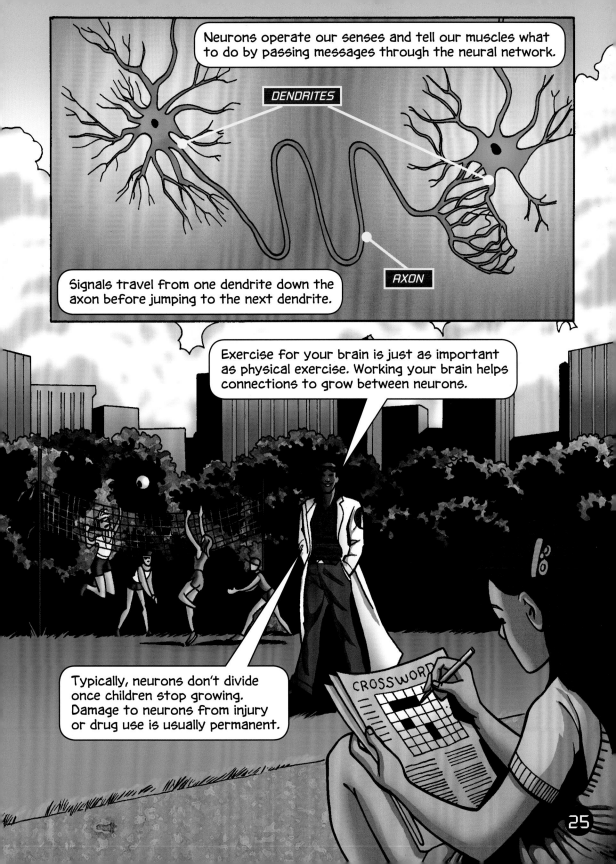

CELL LIFE

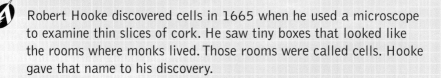

- Robert Hooke discovered cells in 1665 when he used a microscope to examine thin slices of cork. He saw tiny boxes that looked like the rooms where monks lived. Those rooms were called cells. Hooke gave that name to his discovery.

- In 1683, Anton van Leeuwenhoek built a microscope to observe bacteria found in his own mouth. He called them animalcules.

- In 1839, scientists Matthias Schleiden and Theodor Schwann convinced the world that all living things are made of cells. An important part of cell theory is that all cells come from the division of other cells.

- All cells are tiny, but they come in different shapes and sizes. The largest cells are found in frog eggs. They are nearly 1 millimetre (0.04 of an inch) in diameter. The neurons in the spinal cord can be about 90 centimetres (3 feet) long.

- Neurobiology, the study of the brain, is an exciting area of medical research. Scientists use Magnetic Resonance Imaging (MRI) to take pictures of active neurons. These colour photos show which parts of the brain are active when a person plays music or solves crossword puzzles.

- Cell division is a complicated process. Damage to cells may cause them to divide and reproduce incorrectly. When this happens, cells grow in places they should not. The resulting disease is called cancer.

One tool biologists use to study cells is called a cell culture. A cell culture is a sample of cells that is kept alive in the laboratory through continuous cell division. In 1951, cells were taken from a woman who had cancer. Her cells have been dividing ever since. Scientists use these cells in their research.

 Dehydration is more dangerous than starvation because the cytoplasm of cells is made mostly of water. Without water, nothing inside the cell will work correctly. Humans can survive without eating for much longer than they can go without water because cells can use energy stored in fat cells.

MORE ABOUT

SUPER SCIENTIST

Real name: Maxwell Axiom
Height: 1.86 m (6 ft 1 in.)
Weight: 87 kg (13 st. 10 lb)
Eyes: Brown Hair: None

Super capabilities: super intelligence; able to shrink to the size of an atom; sunglasses give X-ray vision; lab coat allows for travel through time and space

Origin: Since birth, Max Axiom seemed destined for greatness. His mother, a marine biologist, taught her son about the mysteries of the sea. His father, a nuclear physicist and volunteer park warden, showed Max the wonders of Earth and sky.

One day while Max was hiking in the hills, a megacharged lightning bolt struck him with blinding fury. When he awoke, Max discovered a new-found energy and set out to learn as much about science as possible. He travelled the globe studying every aspect of the subject. Then he was ready to share his knowledge and new identity with the world. He had become Max Axiom, Super Scientist.

GLOSSARY

amino acid basic building block of protein that contains nitrogen. Amino acids can be made by the body or ingested through eating foods with protein.

ATP molecule that provides energy to cells

cellulose substance from which the cell walls of plants are made

DNA genetic material that carries all the instructions needed to make a living thing and keep it working. DNA stands for deoxyribonucleic acid.

gene part of every cell that carries physical and behavioural information passed from parents to their children

glucose natural sugar found in plants that gives energy to living things

metabolism process of changing food into energy

mitosis process of cell division where one nucleus divides into two, creating two identical cells

nucleus the part of a cell that gives directions to the rest of the cell

organelle small structure in a cell that performs a specific function and is surrounded by its own membrane

photosynthesis process by which green plants make their food

plankton microscopic plants and animals that live in water

stem cell cell from which other types of cells can develop

FIND OUT MORE

Books

Cells and Life Processes (Science Essentials series), Denise Walker (Evans, 2010)

Cells, Tissues, and Organs (The Human Machine series), Richard Spilsbury (Heinemann Library, 2009)

Micro-organisms (Super Science series) (Franklin Watts, 2010)

The World of the Cell (Cells and Life series), Robert Sneddon (Raintree, 2008)

Websites

www.cellsalive.com
Find out more about plant and animal cells on this website, which has lots of amazing pictures, animations, puzzles, and quizzes.

www.sciencemuseum.org.uk
Visit the Science Museum's website and click on "Your body" then on "What do your cells do?" You can learn more about cells and see some great pictures up-close.

INDEX